Contra...
a pro-life guide

Dr O E O Hotonu
MB ChB BSc (Hons) MRCOG MPhil

CHRISTIAN INFLUENCE IN A SECULAR WORLD

First printed in March 2005

ISBN 1 901086 28 3

Published by The Christian Institute
PO Box 1, Newcastle upon Tyne, NE7 7EF

The Christian Institute is a Company Limited by Guarantee, registered in England as a charity. Company No. 263 4440, Charity No. 100 4774.

Contents

Acknowledgments

The Christian Institute gratefully acknowledges the advice and support of Chris Richards and Pam Sims in the writing of this book and for providing the introduction. We are also thankful to all those who have offered comments and suggestions on earlier drafts.

About this book

This book seeks to explain the difference between those contraceptives which can act to destroy a human embryo and those which, according to the best available medical evidence, do not. The book is designed to provide information not instruction. The author and publisher cannot be responsible for any error, omission or dated material. This book is not a substitute for the advice your doctor may give you based on his or her knowledge of any medical conditions you may have. The author and publisher assume no responsibility for any outcome of the use of any contraceptive or other method considered in this book either in a programme of self-care or under medical supervision.

Introduction

The aim of this book is to provide background knowledge on how contraceptives work. As a result we hope that Christian readers will be better equipped to make well-informed ethical decisions. Above all else the book explains the difference between those contraceptives which can act to destroy a human embryo and those which, according to the best available medical evidence, do not.

The use of contraceptives raises other ethical issues, for example whether a Christian couple should decide never to have children even though there are no medical reasons not to. Space does not permit consideration of these in a book of this size.

Historically, Christians have not always shared today's generally positive ethical attitude to contraceptives. Their use was almost universally rejected until 1930 when the Anglican Church eased its sanction in limited circumstances.[1] Over subsequent decades much of the Protestant Church has followed its lead. Nowadays the ethics of contraception are rarely considered in our churches and most Protestant couples enter marriage without reservation about their use. However, we have recently discovered more about the start of early life and the ways in which contraceptives affect this. These mechanisms vary with each form of contraceptive and this knowledge needs to inform our decisions.

Throughout the book we assume that contraceptives are used only in the God-given context for sexual intercourse - that of marriage. It can be argued that the availability of contraception has promoted fornication and adultery. There is the false expectation of sexual activity without the consequence of pregnancy. The widespread availability of the condom has led to the illusion of freedom from sexually transmitted infections. The result has been untold emotional damage, a breakdown in marriage, rising levels of unwanted pregnancies often resulting in abortions, and epidemic levels of sexually transmitted infections (STIs).

Even when reserved for marriage, the use of contraceptives raises several important ethical issues, which the Protestant Church is only beginning to recognize. Since the development of the oral contraceptive in the 1950s we now know more about how the Pill interacts with fertilisation and early life, although there is still more to discover. However, it has become clear that *the separation of sexual union from procreation by the use of medicines is difficult to do effectively and precisely*. This fact raises an important ethical issue.

When does life begin?
There are strong biological and theological reasons for understanding that life begins at fertilisation. This is the moment of the sudden, complete and defining genetic unity of the mother and father. Their 'one flesh' becomes a cellular reality. Miscarriages apart, if the growth of new life is to be stopped after this moment something destructive in intent needs to be done.

Attempts have been made to define the start of life at other times. These definitions are usually based on either the level of fetal dependence marked by events such as implantation and birth, or the presence of some intrinsic quality such as fetal responsiveness. However, we should reject valuing human life in this way. Human life is made in the image of God. (See Genesis 1:27) Its value has a heavenly rather than an earthly currency and a person's status defies such subjective definitions based on ability or dependence.

There is also strong evidence from the Bible that life is recognized from conception (see Psalm 51:5 'Surely I was sinful at birth, sinful from the time my mother conceived me.'). An alternative model involves the infusion of the soul at some stage in embryo development bestowing upon it the status of life. This model necessarily requires unifying of a soulless 'pre-body' and the newly formed soul, an event for which there is no hint of biblical support. It would be hard to know how to decide when this event had taken place. It would also be hard to understand how Jesus, who was fully man and fully God, could have been conceived by Mary through the Holy Spirit but did not become a life until some days later (See Matthew 1:20 and Hebrews 2:14, 17).

Protecting life in uncertainty
Christians recognize the sanctity of all human life. If life does begin at fertilisation, this has profound ethical implications for the use of any contraceptive which acts to threaten the survival or implantation of an early embryo. We know that some contraceptives, such as the IUD, do indeed work primarily in this way. These are denoted by a cross in this book.

With other contraceptives there are at least two sources of uncertainty about their effect. For some contraceptives, such as the mini-pill, we cannot be sure of their predominant mechanism of action. For others, such as the Combined Oral Contraceptive Pill (COCP), we understand their major effect but cannot be sure that they always work in this way in any month in any individual. Appendix 1 contains a detailed discussion of the mode of action of the COCP. It is tempting to ignore possible serious ethical consequences when things seem uncertain. But should we do so, when life is (or may be) at risk, especially when we can avoid doing so? In some rare circumstances a particular form of contraception may be medically necessary. But for most people, the primary intention is simply not to conceive. So, is the risk worth taking than a human embryo may be lost?

Life in the real world

Issues raised in this book could have direct implications. Whether we are in a position of church leadership, prescribe or use contraception we may have to reconsider a matter that we had thought was already sorted.

During the 1970's there was a mass turning away by Christian women from use of the old fashioned plastic intrauterine device when its abortifacient mode of action was realised (with a number of babies born as a result!). In more recent years there have been various pill scares, heightened by the media. We do not want to start a panic. The intention is not to unhelpfully focus on the past but to inform future decisions. We do want people to thoughtfully and prayerfully re-examine this aspect of their lives and possibly make adjustments to their contraceptive practice and/or teaching on the subject. The Christian response is to act on what we know not to dwell on what we did not know in the past.

This book will inform us and bring us up to date as far as possible. The information has practical value. Clergy providing pre-marital courses should promote obviously pro-life methods of contraception. Christian women themselves, and their marriage partners, should seek such methods: for those already on the pill note the issues raised in appendix 1. At the end of the day we can only be as well informed as possible and humbly come before God and pray that He will enlighten our consciences according to His will.

Chris Richards MA MB BS FRCPCH
Consultant Paediatrician, The Royal Victoria Infirmary, Newcastle upon Tyne

Pamela Sims MB ChB, FRCS, FRCOG
Consultant Obstetrician and Gynaecologist, Northumbria Healthcare NHS Trust

The Key

Throughout this book this key is used to indicate whether or not a contraceptive acts without destroying a human embryo.

 A pro-life method which does not destroy human embryos.

 Not pro-life, a method which does destroy human embryos.

 We cannot be sure whether or not human embryos are destroyed with this method. Pro-life doctors argue about the evidence.

 A pro-life method when the treatment is first given but the contraceptive effect may wear off before the time for renewal and so may cause human embryos to be destroyed.

 Too new to have any reliable published evidence on its pro-life status.

Glossary

Conception

Usually, for a pre-menopausal woman, every month an egg comes from a woman's ovary (ovulation). During sexual intercourse, the man's sperm are discharged and travel from the vagina, through the womb and into a fallopian tube. If a released egg is there, fertilisation or conception, that is, the union of the egg with one sperm, may take place. This newly formed human being or embryo takes five days to travel from the fallopian tube to the womb where the embryo becomes attached, or implants, and continues to grow and develop.

Failure rates

The intention of using a contraceptive method is to prevent pregnancies occurring following sexual intercourse. However, no contraceptive works perfectly. Sometimes they fail.

This book describes the 'failure rate' of different methods of contraception for women. The failure rate refers to the percentage of women who become pregnant within the first year of use.

The failure rates are given as percentages and can be reported in two ways.

First, by describing how effective the method is *in theory* – that is, how many pregnancies occur even after 'perfect use'. Secondly, the pregnancy rate can be described in terms of 'typical use' – that is, how many pregnancies occur *in practice* for the average user.

For example, although the combined oral contraceptive pill is extremely effective with a low failure rate if used *perfectly*, the failure rate after *typical use* is higher because the pill will be ineffective if the user forgets to take it. Similarly the condom is a reasonably effective method in a committed, mature couple but has a much greater failure rate in the young and inexperienced.

The failure rates are quoted, unless otherwise stated, from the latest edition of Contraceptive Technology – a standard medical reference book on contraception.[2]

Description
A brief outline of the contraceptive is given under this heading.

Mode of Action
Different contraceptives work in different ways. Some prevent conception, but others do not – they act later by preventing an embryo (already conceived) from implanting in the womb. Therefore any product that prevents implantation works by causing an abortion (see box "Definition of abortion and pregnancy" on page 12) because the embryo is expelled from the womb and the pregnancy does not progress. Strictly speaking it is not a contraceptive at all – because conception has already taken place.

Some contraceptives can work in different ways on different occasions. For example, the mini-pill can act in three ways. The first two modes of action are contraceptive. However, the third prevents an embryo implanting in the womb. In this case if one mini-pill failed in its first two modes of action, conception would take place and then the third mode of action may occur. It is impossible to determine which mode of action is occurring following sexual intercourse. It could be one or any combination of them.

This book describes all the known potential modes of action for each method of contraception.

In addition, there is no research into the residual effects of hormonal contraceptives when their use is ceased. From a pro-life perspective this is an area of biological uncertainty. Where this is relevant to a particular contraceptive, appropriate comments have been made in this book.

Side Effects

All forms of contraception have potential side effects. Where possible, an indication is given as to whether the side effects are common or less common. As far as possible, we have attempted to ensure that the definitions used are in accordance with the appropriate manufacturer's patient information sheet.

The definition of abortion and pregnancy

It is important to note that the legal definition of abortion was changed in 1983 so as to exclude actions which prevent an embryo implanting in the womb.[3] This book takes the view that destroying human embryos in this way is morally wrong and so from a moral point of view the legal definition of abortion should never have been changed. The definition of pregnancy was similarly changed so that it was only said to occur when the embryo implants in the womb. This book considers that pregnancy begins at conception.

Condom

Failure Rates
Perfect use = 2%
Typical use = 15%

Description
In appearance an unused condom is like a deflated balloon. Most condoms are made from latex (rubber). However, for people with a rubber allergy, there are condoms made from polyurethane (plastic). The condom fits over the erect penis. Some condoms are manufactured with a spermicide coating.

Mode of Action
1) Condoms are known as a barrier method because they act as a physical barrier between the sperm and egg and prevent them meeting.
2) The barrier method does not cause the loss of an embryo.
3) It could be used together with a spermicide (see Spermicide section), which may help kill sperm that may bypass the condom.

Side effects
This method has few side effects, but may cause allergic reactions.[4] The failure of this method is usually related to the motivation and experience of the user. It is most likely to fail in the young and the inexperienced. It is also likely to fail if the condom is used with oil based lubricants such as baby oil, Vaseline or petroleum jelly as these products can damage the latex within 15 minutes.[5]

Femidom®

Failure Rates
Perfect use = 5%
Typical use = 21%

Description
The female condom, Femidom®, is made from polyurethane. Femidom® is tubular but wider than a condom with a thin plastic ring at either end to aid fitting. Femidom® is placed in the vagina. It contains a non-spermicidal silicone lubricant.

Mode of Action
1) The Femidom® is known as a barrier method because it acts as a physical barrier between the sperm and egg and prevents them meeting.
2) The barrier method does not cause the loss of an embryo.
3) It should be used together with a spermicide (see Spermicides section), which kills any sperm that may bypass the Femidom®.

Side effects
This method has few side effects, but may cause an allergic reaction to the spermicide used in conjunction with the Femidom®.[6]
The failure of this method is particularly related to the motivation and experience of the user. It is most likely to fail in the young and the inexperienced. In contrast to the latex condom, the plastic used in the Femidom® is not affected by oil based lubricants.[7]

Diaphragm, cap, sponge

Failure Rates
Diaphragm (with spermicidal cream or jelly):
Perfect use = 6%, Typical use = 16%
Cap (with spermicidal cream or jelly):
Perfect use = 9-26%, Typical use = 16-32%
Sponge:
Perfect use = 9-20%, Typical use = 16-32%

Description
These are barrier methods but are used only by women. They are all made of latex (rubber), or in the case of the sponge, polyurethane foam. All are used with a spermicide. Initially trained personnel, who also teach the user what to do, must fit the diaphragm or cap.

Mode of Action
1) None of these methods cause the loss of an embryo.
2) The diaphragm covers the cervix and part of the vagina, whereas the cap and the sponge are designed to fit over the cervix alone. This is why the failure rates vary for each method.
3) The cap stays in place by suction but it is often dislodged during sex.
4) The sponge is impregnated with spermicide and protects for up to 24 hours.[8] However, like the cap, it is also commonly dislodged during sex. Nevertheless it is popular in the US where roughly 250 million *Today* sponges were sold from 1983 to 1995.[9]
5) Both the cap and sponge have relatively high failure rates – especially in young fertile women.

Side Effects

Like the condom, these barrier methods may also cause an allergic reaction. In addition, the diaphragm may increase the risk of urinary infections. Furthermore, in the USA, it has been reported that each year 3 in every 100,000 of vaginal barrier users develop Toxic Shock Syndrome, a rare but serious illness that can cause, amongst other things, fever, diarrhoea, vomiting and, very infrequently, death.[10]

Spermicide

Failure Rates
Perfect use = 18%
Typical use = 29%

These failure rates are based on weak and limited studies. These rates are for the use of spermicides alone, but spermicides should be used in conjunction with another form of contraception.

Description
Spermicides are found in various forms including pessaries, foam, gel, jelly, cream and tablets. Condoms may also be lubricated with spermicide. The usual active ingredient in all spermicides is nonoxynol-9.

Mode of Action
Spermicides kill sperm and are used together with barrier methods of contraception such as the condom or diaphragm.

Side effects
Spermicides may occasionally cause a mild allergic reaction in susceptible users.[11] Spermicides do not cause the loss of an embryo, but previous studies suggested a possible link between the use of them and abnormalities found in babies born to users of spermicides. However, these studies were subsequently found to be faulty and more recent research has not found this link. Therefore it is believed that the two are not associated.[12]

Progestogen-only pill

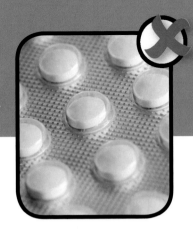

Failure Rates[13]
Perfect use = 0.5%
Typical use = 5%

Description
The progestogen-only pill (POP) is also known as the 'mini-pill' because it only contains one female hormone, a progestogen. POP products include Femulen, Micronor, Microval, Noriday, Neogest, Norgeston and more recently Cerazette® (see next section).

The mini-pill must be taken at approximately the same time each day because its contraceptive strength decreases rapidly after 24 hours. The mini-pill is often offered to women who cannot take the combined oral contraceptive pill (see later), which contains a progestogen and another female hormone called oestrogen. Therefore the mini-pill may be given to older women who smoke, because oestrogen greatly increases the risk of them developing a blood clot. The mini-pill may also be given to nursing mothers, because the oestrogen in the combined oral contraceptive pill reduces and may stop milk production.

Mode of Action
The mini-pill works primarily in three ways. Two of the methods are contraceptive.

1) The mini-pill acts by stopping the release of an egg.

The mini-pill is not good at stopping the release of an egg. In his book about contraception Professor Guillebaud mentions a Swedish study that showed that 40% of the participants still released an egg every month despite taking the mini-pill correctly.[14]

In practice, family planning experts claim that women whose periods have remained unchanged whilst they are taking the mini-pill are still producing eggs, whilst those women who experience either no periods or prolonged periods of time between menstrual bleeds are not producing eggs.[15]

2) The mini-pill acts by thickening and decreasing the mucus from the cervix in order to stop the sperm reaching the egg.

Thickened cervical mucus is supposed to stop sperm from reaching the egg because they cannot move through the altered mucus very easily. However, a study in rabbits has shown that thickened cervical mucus does not result in all sperm being blocked[16] and therefore may not be able to prevent the sperm reaching the egg. Also a four year study in women taking a progestogen-only pill from day 5 to 25 of their cycle showed that 5% of sperm were able to penetrate cervical mucus between days 9 to 16.[17]

The uncertainty of the above mechanisms show how it is possible to become pregnant even if taking the mini-pill perfectly.

3) The mini-pill thins the lining of the womb.

This is not contraceptive, but it is this action that may cause the loss of an embryo. Normally the lining of the womb thickens in readiness to receive an embryo. The mini-pill may stop this happening making it almost impossible for the embryo to implant and to develop normally. Support for this effect of the mini-pill comes from studies in infertile women undergoing in vitro fertilisation. In these women the pregnancy rate is low when the lining of the womb is very thin.[18] This happens because the embryo is not able to implant into the very thin lining of the womb. In the Pharmacists' handbook, *Martindale*, it is clearly asserted that the thinning of the lining of the womb makes conditions "… unfavourable for implantation of any fertilised ova".[19] Thus it is possible for conception to occur whilst taking the mini-pill, but the embryo may be lost due to failure to implant in the thinned lining of the womb.

In summary, despite a level of uncertainty about the mode of action at a particular point in time, it is known that it is less effective in preventing ovulation than some other hormonal contraceptives and the effect of the mini-pill is highly dependent on when it is taken. All of this means that the mini-pill is very much more likely to destroy human embryos than, say, the combined oral contraceptive.

In addition, there is no research into the residual effects of hormonal contraceptives when their use is ceased. In the case of the progestogen-only pill it is unknown how long the lining of the womb is affected by the presence of the hormone in a woman's system. From a pro-life perspective, it is an area of biological uncertainty as to whether an embryo will fail to implant because of the residual effects of the hormone. A woman with concerns in this area would look to use a barrier method of contraception until after her second period[20] when ceasing to use the progestogen-only pill.

Side Effects

The mini-pill may cause irregular vaginal bleeding, non-cancerous cysts to develop in the ovaries, depression, acne, weight changes and breast tenderness.[21] It can also affect the fallopian tube where fertilisation takes place so that the embryo does not move normally to the womb. If the embryo grows in the tube instead of the womb, this is known as an ectopic pregnancy and it can be life threatening to the mother.

The British National Formulary states that an increased risk of breast cancer is a possible side-effect, but this may be due to the age of the user or the fact that women on the mini-pill tend to have themselves examined more frequently. The risk disappears gradually during the 10 years after stopping and there is no excess risk by 10 years.[22]

Cerazette®[23]

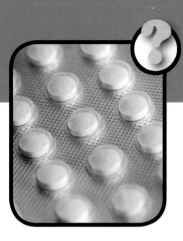

Failure Rate
The manufacturers state that the failure rate is similar to the combined oral contraceptive pill (see next section).

Description
This is a new progestogen-only pill which contains the progestogen desogestrel. Like other types of mini-pill, it is often recommended to women who smoke or for nursing mothers (see section on Progestogen-only pill).

Mode of Action
According to the manufacturers, Cerazette® has the following modes of action:

1) Like other mini-pills it thickens the cervical mucus to stop the sperm reaching the egg.

2) Unlike other mini-pills it is able to prevent ovulation almost 100% of the time like the combined oral contraceptive pill. In one study when Cerazette® was deliberately discontinued after it had been taken for 56 days continuously, ovulation occurred on average 17 days after the last Cerazette® pill had been taken (range 7 – 30 days).[24]   Normally women on progestogen-only pills (POPs) are advised to take their pill within a three hour window each day, so as to maintain the effectiveness of the pill. It must be taken at the same time every day or with at most a three hour delay. New evidence presented at the 8th Congress of the European Society

of Contraception in June 2004 showed that Cerazette®
consistently inhibits ovulation even when tablets are taken
12 hours late.[25] Therefore the manufacturers of Cerazette®
now recommend that its window be extended to 12 hours.[26]

Note: The manufacturers warn that Cerazette® may cause ectopic
pregnancies. If true, this warning demonstrates two things: (i)
ovulation can occur; and, (ii) sperm can penetrate the mucus. The
question then arrises as to whether an embryo would or would not
implant in the lining of the womb. We take a different view to Prof.
Guillebaud, a family planning expert, who believes that Cerazette® is
"…entirely secure for those who hold the absolutist ethical position
that blocking implantation is a form of abortion".[27] Though the
manufacturers make this statement about ectopic pregnancies
we have not found any studies on whether Cerazette® affects the
lining of the womb.[28] At present it is impossible to be certain that
Cerazette® will not cause an embryo to be lost. The issues are finely
balanced and in some respects parallel to those on the combined
pill. Appendix 1 contains a fuller discussion of the mode of action of
the combined pill.

In addition, there is no research into the residual effects of hormonal
contraceptives when their use is ceased. In the case of Cerazette®
we cannot be sure whether this pill continues to act after ovulation
has returned due to the presence of the hormone in a woman's
system. This will be of concern to those who conclude that this pill
does have a post-fertilisation effect (see appendix 1). From a pro-
life perspective, it is an area of biological uncertainty as to whether
an embryo will fail to implant because of the residual effects of the
hormone. A woman with concerns in this area would look to use
a barrier method of contraception until after her second period[29]
when ceasing to use Cerazette®.

Side Effects

A common side effect is irregular vaginal bleeding[30], which is more common than with the other mini-pills and may be of longer duration. However, after a couple of months, bleeding tends to be less frequent. Other common side effects include acne, mood changes, breast pain, nausea and weight increase. Although Cerazette® prevents ovulation, the manufacturers believe that it may still cause ectopic pregnancies (see above).

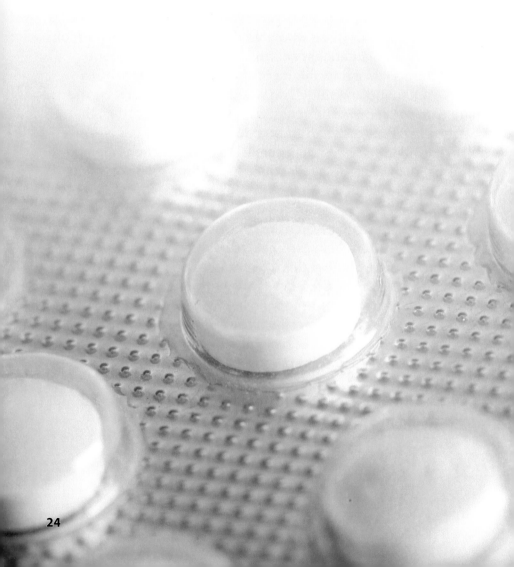

Combined oral contraceptive pill

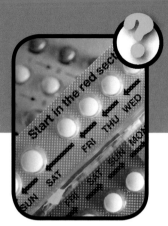

Failure Rate[31]
Perfect use = 0.1%
Typical use = 5%

Description
The combined oral contraceptive pill contains two female hormones, oestrogen and a progestogen. There are about 28 different types of combined pill products available that vary in strength and other factors, but essentially they all work in the same way.

After a period the combined pill is taken daily for three weeks followed by a week when either a sugar pill that does not contain any hormone is taken or no pill is taken at all.

Mode of Action – See appendix 1
The combined pill works in the same three ways as the mini-pill:

1) it stops the release of an egg;
2) it thickens and decreases cervical mucus; and
3) it thins the lining of the womb.

Unlike the mini-pill, the combined pill is believed to be extremely good at stopping the release of an egg and this has always been assumed to be its main action.

As the combined pill has developed over time the oestrogen content has been reduced by the manufacturers. This has led to suggestions that the combined pill does not prevent the release of an egg all the time and therefore, as in the mini-pill user, (see progestogen-only pill section), fertilisation may take place. There is no dispute that the combined pill reduces the depth of the lining of the womb. There is dispute over the effect that this would have in preventing implantation of an embryo. By its very nature, interpreting the evidence on this particular issue is highly complex. For more information about this evidence it is essential to read appendix 1.

In addition, there is no research into the residual effects of hormonal contraceptives when their use is ceased. In the case of the combined pill we cannot be sure whether this pill continues to act after ovulation has returned due to the presence of the hormone in a woman's system. This will be of concern to those who conclude that this pill does have a post-fertilisation effect (see appendix 1). The advice used to be commonly given to women on the combined pill "wait three months before trying for a family". In other words use a barrier method for three months after giving up using the combined pill. The scientific basis for this is unclear and unknown and some would suggest that it is no longer needed.[32] However, from a pro-life perspective, it is an area of biological uncertainty as to whether an embryo will fail to implant because of the residual effects of the hormones. A woman with concerns in this area would look to use a barrier method of contraception until after her second period[33] when ceasing to use the combined pill.

Side Effects
Possible side effects of the combined pill[34] include breast tenderness, headaches, changes in weight, acne and depression. A less common side effect is thrombosis.[35]

There may be an increased risk of breast cancer. Breast cancer has been found slightly more often in women who use the pill than in women who do not. It is not certain whether the pill causes the increased risk of breast cancer. It may be that women using the pill are examined more often, so that breast cancer is noticed earlier. Once a woman stops taking the pill, after ten years the risk of breast cancer is the same as for women who have never used the pill.[36] In long term users, a less common side effect is cervical cancer. However, it is uncertain whether the increased risk of cervical cancer is caused by the pill as it could be due to the effects of sexual behaviour and other factors. The combined pill protects against ovarian and endometrial cancer.[37]

New Products
In 2003 two new products containing combined hormonal contraceptives were introduced.

The first was another oral combined contraceptive pill called *Yasmin®*. It contains a progestogen hormone that is very similar to that found in the body.[38] Its selling point is that it causes fewer side effects than other combined hormone pills on the market and, most notably, that it doesn't cause weight gain and fluid retention. The Scottish Medicine Consortium, however, has not recommended *Yasmin®* because the Consortium believes that the benefits of this product do not justify its financial cost.[39] *Yasmin®* is about five times more expensive than the cheapest combined oral contraceptive pill available. In February 2003, the *British Medical Journal* published a report from Holland about five women who developed blood clots whilst taking *Yasmin®*. These women had no other risk factors that would make them prone to develop a blood clot. The youngest woman, who was only 17 years old, collapsed and died after taking the contraceptive for six months. At post mortem she was found to have had a massive clot in her lung. Another woman developed a clot in her lungs after she had been on *Yasmin®* for only 17 days.[40] However, the Medicines and Healthcare Products Regulatory Agency has reported a study from which the interim results suggest there is no increased risk of blood clots for users of *Yasmin®* when compared to the use of other combined oral contraceptives.[41]

The second new product introduced was *Evra®* which is a contraceptive skin patch. Hormones are released slowly so the patch only has to be changed once a week. Clinical trials have shown that *Evra®* is as effective as oral combined contraceptives although it has a high failure rate in women weighing over 90 kilograms (14 stones).[42] The manufacturers state that the safety and efficacy of *Evra®* was only established in women between 18 and 45 years of age.[43] According to a BBC press report, the manufacturers acknowledge that there have been six reports of fatalities in which the role of the product is said to be unclear.[44]

As well as two new products containing combined hormonal contraception there have also been recent newspaper reports about two forthcoming products.

In December 2003, it was announced that a 'lifestyle' contraceptive pill called *Seasonale®* was to be launched in Britain.[45] *Seasonale®* is taken for 84 days continuously after which a woman has a seven day break, thus a woman only has four periods a year. At the time of this publication *Seasonale®* is not yet available in this country. This is a form of tricycling (see Tricycling section) although some details of the product – such as its effectiveness in suppressing ovulation – are not yet known.

In July 2004, the newspapers announced that a contraceptive ring was to be launched soon in Britain.[46] *NuvaRing®*, a flexible clear ring is inserted into the vagina once a month, releases hormones directly into the bloodstream and therefore uses half the concentration of hormones found in the conventional contraceptive pill. For these reasons, it is reported to have fewer side effects and gives better control of the menstrual cycle than the conventional contraceptive pill. At the time of this publication *NuvaRing®* is not yet available in this country.

Tricycling of the combined oral contraceptive pill (Tricycle regimen[47])

Description

Women who are concerned that use of the combined oral contraceptive pill (COCP) may cause the loss of an embryo can eliminate the risk of ovulating by "tricycling". The COCP is usually taken for 21 days out of every 28 and the time that the pill is not taken is known as the pill-free interval (PFI). During the PFI a woman does not take the pill and, therefore, experiences a rapid fall in pill hormones. This rapid fall may cause some women to ovulate and subsequently to conceive.

Tricycling involves taking three packets of active pills in a row and then reducing the PFI from 7 days to 4.[48] The mode of action is essentially the same as for the COCP however the aim of tricycling is to completely suppress ovulation. Prof. Guillebaud, a family planning expert, recommends this practice for a variety of reasons, not just pro-life concerns.[49]

While tricycling may be recommended by pro-life doctors for the above reason, other doctors are reluctant to recommend taking the pill in a way other than stated on the packet.

Intrauterine contraceptive device: Copper containing coil

Failure Rates
Perfect use = 0.6%
Typical use = 0.8%

Description
A copper containing coil is an intrauterine contraceptive device (IUCD) that is inserted into a woman's womb. It can remain in place for up to five years after which its effectiveness decreases, although one of the newer coils, the *T-Safe®CU 380A*, is effective for up to eight years. The coil may contain either the metal copper, for example, *Multiload®Cu250*, *Flexi T®300*, or a mixture of copper and silver as in the *Nova T®380*.

The newest type of coil is the *GyneFix®*, which consists of 6 copper cylinders attached to a knotted plastic-like thread. The knot is inserted into the roof of the womb.

The coil has to be fitted by trained personnel. The copper containing coils are commonly used as 'emergency contraception'.

Mode of Action
The coil works in three ways. The first two are contraceptive. The third is not.
1) It destroys sperm and egg, thus preventing them from meeting.[50]

The body produces cells that eat sperm and the egg. The womb sees the coil as alien and tries to destroy it. As part of this response, the lining of womb becomes inflamed and cells are produced that are able to eat any substances that 'don't belong' to the body, such as sperm and the egg. These "killer cells" are not only found in the womb but also in the tube leading to the womb where fertilisation usually takes place.[51]

2) Copper containing coils can also have a direct chemical effect either by immobilising the sperm or killing the sperm or egg before they meet.[52]

3) Copper containing coils may also cause the loss of an embryo. There are two ways in which this can happen.[53] First, as mentioned previously, these coils can cause inflammation of the lining of the womb, a condition that is thought to block the implantation of the embryo. Secondly, the copper is also poisonous to the early embryo.

Side Effects
There is an uncommon risk with inserting the copper containing coil that may result in making a hole in the womb, the bladder or the bowel[54] In experienced hands, this risk is 1 per 1,000 insertions or less.[55]

Coils may be expelled from the womb spontaneously. This affects between 2% to 10% of users within the first year and may occur without the woman being aware that it has happened.[56]

Over 50% of pregnancies that occur in the womb whilst the coil is in place end in spontaneous abortion. When the coil is removed early in pregnancy, the rate of spontaneous abortion is about 20%.[57]

10% of women who become pregnant with a coil in place will have an ectopic pregnancy.[58]

These coils may also cause heavier periods and an increase in period pain. However, these may be symptomatic of a more serious problem.[59] There is an increased risk of pelvic infection around the time of insertion of the coil.[60]

Intrauterine contraceptive device: Mirena® intrauterine system

Failure Rates
Perfect use = 0.1%
Typical use = 0.1%

Description
The Mirena® intrauterine system is an intrauterine contraceptive device (IUCD) that is inserted into a woman's womb. It contains the hormone Levonorgestrel (which is similar to the hormone progesterone). It can remain in place for up to five years after which its effectiveness decreases although its contraceptive effectiveness may reduce in the last year.

Mode of Action
The hormone containing coil, Mirena®, has several contraceptive mechanisms.

1) The hormone within this coil has a similar effect to that of the mini-pill, (see Progestogen-only pill section) with the result that sperm are less able to pass through cervical mucus.[61]
2) Like the copper containing coils, it also causes the production of cells that eat sperm.[62]
3) Mirena® can stop the release of an egg.

However, the manufacturer of Mirena® says that ovulation occurs in some women.[63] This is confirmed in one study where women who were using this intrauterine system were found to be ovulating.[64] Because ovulation may begin again, the Mirena® intrauterine system may also cause the loss of an embryo during the last year of use. This is because Mirena® causes thinning of the lining of the womb. This action can prevent an early embryo from implanting in the womb.[65]

Prof Guillebaud, a family planning expert, goes further. He states that "unfavourable cervical mucus is not always observed and we know that ovulation still occurs in most cycles."[66] He also comments "Although there are no direct data, the very rare cases of ectopic pregnancy in women using this method provide indirect evidence that fertilisation can occur."[67] He concludes "…we must remain unsure that the *Levonorgestrel-IUS* absolutely never operates post-fertilisation."[68]

In addition, there is no research into the residual effects of hormonal contraceptives when their use is ceased. In the case of Mirena® we cannot be sure whether it continues to act after ovulation has returned due to the presence of the hormone in a woman's system. It is thought that there is a rapid return of fertility after the removal of Mirena®.[69] However, from a pro-life perspective, it is an area of biological uncertainty as to whether an embryo will fail to implant because of the residual effects of the hormone. A woman with concerns in this area would look to use a barrier method of contraception until after her first period[70] when ceasing to use Mirena®.

Side Effects
Common side effects of the Mirena® intrauterine system include weight gain, depression, headache, pelvic or back pain, nausea, acne, painful periods and tender or painful breasts. An uncommon side effect can include problems with inserting the coil that may result in making a hole in the womb, the bladder or the bowel.[71]

Coils may be expelled from the womb spontaneously. This affects between 2% to 10% of users within the first year and may occur without the woman being aware that it has happened.[72]

Over 50% of pregnancies that occur in the womb whilst the coil is in place end in spontaneous abortion. When the coil is removed early in pregnancy, the rate of spontaneous abortion is about 20%.[73] If pregnancy occurs whilst the Mirena® coil is in the womb, the risk of having an ectopic pregnancy is less than 1%.[74]

Mirena® users have lighter or no periods with little or no period pain compared to users of copper containing coils. Users are also less likely to develop pelvic infections.[75] With Mirena® a small amount of hormone goes into the body and therefore users may experience similar side effects to the users of the mini-pill, for example cysts on the ovaries, and breast tenderness.[76]

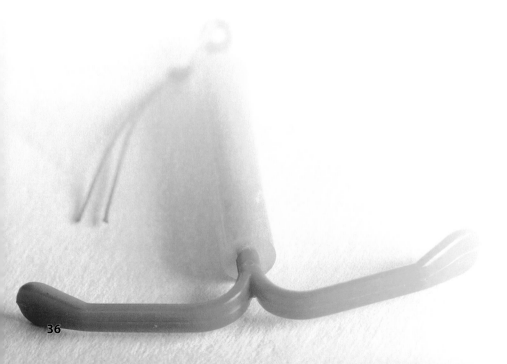

Implanon®, Norplant

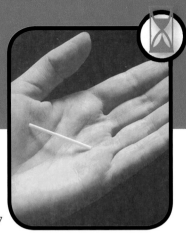

Failure rates

Two studies looked at a total of 9,732 women using Implanon® for a year, and found that there were no pregnancies.[77]

Norplant gained a bad reputation because of difficulties with removing it and the fact that it caused troublesome side effects. Therefore it was discontinued and since April 2001 the implant Implanon® has been available instead.

Description

Implanon® is a single flexible rod that contains the progestogen, etonogestrel. The rod is injected under the skin of the upper arm. Normally it is effective for up to 3 years but, in overweight women, it may not provide effective contraception during the third year and an earlier replacement is recommended.[78] Implanon® is designed as a long-term contraceptive.

Mode of Action

Implanon® appears to work in a similar way to other progestogen-only contraceptives.
1) It can increase the thickness of cervical mucus, thus preventing the movement of sperm.[79]
2) It can thin the lining of the womb.
In addition
3) It prevents ovulation effectively for 2 years. There is no *conclusive evidence* at present to show that Implanon® causes the loss of an embryo.

One study showed that, based on hormone levels in users of Implanon®, none of the participants released an egg during the first two years whilst using it.[80] Another study, which used a blood test and an ultrasound scan to look at the ovaries of women using Implanon®, showed that fewer than 5% of users had begun to release eggs 30 months after the implant had been inserted.[81] Furthermore, although Implanon® thins the lining of the womb, it does so to a lesser extent than other progestogen-containing contraceptives. Therefore it is unclear at present whether the reduced effect of Implanon® will minimise the likelihood of this mechanism leading to the loss of an embryo. This is only relevant when the effect of preventing ovulation wears off.

In addition, there is no research into the residual effects of hormonal contraceptives when their use is ceased. In the case of Implanon® we cannot be sure whether it continues to act after ovulation has returned due to the presence of the hormone in a woman's system. This will be of concern to those who conclude Implanon® does have a post-fertilisation effect when it is nearing the time of replacement. In his book *Contraception*, Prof. Guillebaud states that the hormone is undetectable in blood samples one week after Implanon® was removed.[82] However, from a pro-life perspective, it is an area of biological uncertainty as to whether an embryo will fail to implant because of the residual effects of the hormone. A woman with concerns in this area would look to use a barrier method of contraception until after her second period[83] when ceasing to use Implanon®.

Side effects
Common side effects include acne, breast pain, irregular bleeding and painful menstruation. Uncommon side effects include itching, sickness and diarrhoea and pelvic cramping.[84] At present, there is no evidence that Implanon® causes ectopic pregnancies.

More frequent replacement of the hormone implant

According to the manufacturers, Implanon® should be replaced at the end of three years of use.[85]

Research has shown that near the time the hormone implant is due to be replaced ovulation may occur. One study found that 30 months (2½ years) after the implant was given 2 women ovulated during a total of four cycles.[86] A way of avoiding any risk of ovulating whilst using this method of contraception is by shortening the replacement interval. So a woman could ask her doctor to replace her implant after 2½ years.[87] It would be for the doctor to decide whether to agree with this request in each particular case.

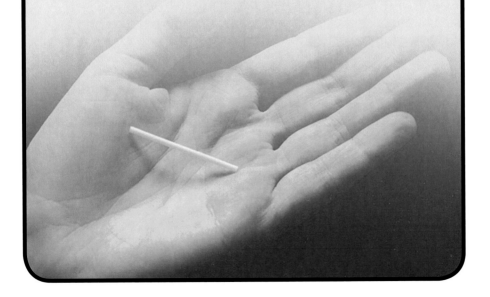

Depo-Provera, Noristerat

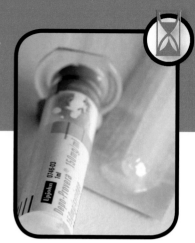

Failure Rates

Depo-Provera:
Perfect use = 0.3%
Typical use = 3%
Noristerat:
No percentage figures available, but it has been documented that there were up to 2 pregnancies amongst 100 women using Noristerat for a year.[88]

Description

Depo-Provera consists of the progestogen medroxyprogesterone and is injected into the user every three months. It is often recommended for women who prefer not to take tablets. Noristerat consists of a progestogen, called norethisterone. Noristerat must be given every 8 weeks.

Mode of Action

Both injectable contraceptives act in a similar way to the other contraceptives that contain a progestogen. (See Progestogen-only pill section)

1) However, because they contain a high concentration of hormones they are able to stop the release of the egg. This is their primary action.
2) They thicken and decrease cervical mucus.
3) They thin the lining of the womb.

Both injectable contraceptives may cause the loss of an embryo as the time for replacement draws near. The injectable contraceptives are more efficient than the combined pill at stopping the release of an egg. However in some women, as the time for another injection approaches, the ovaries start to become active again.[89] Like the mini-pill, neither Depo-Provera nor Noristerat are able to completely stop the progress of sperm and therefore should an egg be released, fertilisation may occur. The resultant embryo may be unable to implant in the womb because of its thinned lining, and is lost.

In addition, there is no research into the residual effects of hormonal contraceptives when their use is ceased. In the case of injectable contraceptives, we cannot be sure whether these continue to act after ovulation has returned due to the presence of the hormone in a woman's system. This will be of concern to those who conclude that Depo-Provera does have a post-fertilisation effect when it is nearing the time of replacement. Family planning expert, Prof. Guillebaud, states that the return of fertility takes, on average, 5½ months.[90] He also states that Depo-Provera acts in the average women for 15 weeks after injection. From a pro-life perspective, it is an area of biological uncertainty as to whether an embryo will fail to implant because of the residual effects of the hormone. A woman with concerns in this area would look to use a barrier method of contraception until after her first period[91] when ceasing to use Depo-Provera.

Side effects
A disadvantage is that once the drug is injected it cannot be removed. The side effects of Depo-Provera and Noristerat include weight change, irregular bleeding or an absence of bleeding. Less common side effects include breast pain and depression.[92] A 1984 study found on average a 9 month delay in the return of fertility after treatment is stopped.[93] In Depo-Provera users, thinning of the bone has been reported.[94] This is reversible once treatment has stopped.

A recent study suggested a link between injectable contraceptives and an increased risk of sexually transmitted diseases.[95] This is due to the combination of three factors. First there is the action of the hormones in thinning the lining of the vagina making it more vulnerable to infection. Secondly, the user may not be using a barrier method. Thirdly, the user may have multiple sexual partners.

More frequent injections

Research has shown that near the time that the Depo-Provera injection is due to be replaced ovulation may occur.[96] A method aimed at suppressing ovulation is to shorten the replacement interval. Thus, a woman could request that the hormone injection be given every 10 weeks instead of the usual 12.[97]

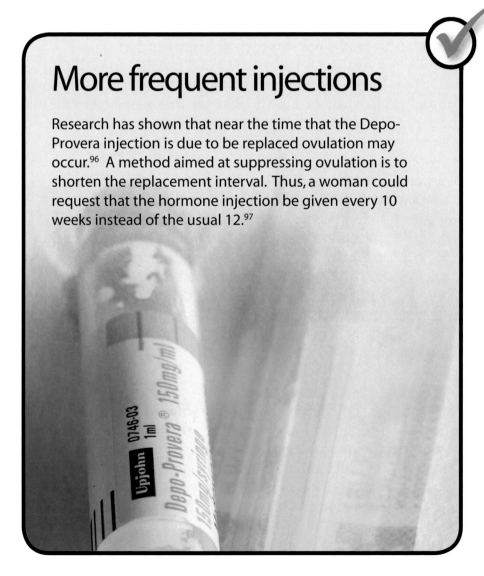

Natural birth control

PERSONA

Failure Rates
Withdrawal Method
Perfect use = 4% , Typical use = 27%
Persona
Perfect use = 6%[98]
Rhythm Methods
Perfect use = 1-9%, Typical use = 25%

Description
Natural birth control includes various techniques that detect the beginning and end of a women's fertile time, and a method that prevents the sperm and egg meeting. Further information on natural birth control techniques can be found at the following websites: http://epigee.org/guide/natural.html; and http://www.fertilityuk.org/index.html.

Mode of Action
1) None of these methods cause the loss of an embryo.

2) The *withdrawal method* involves the man removing his penis just before sperm are released. The man requires a high degree of self-control in order to do this technique properly. It has been claimed that sexual pleasure may be diminished[99] but it costs nothing and requires no devices or chemicals. However, even if the withdrawal is properly timed, the pre-ejaculate fluid could contain sperm.[100]

3) *Persona* is a hand-held monitor for women that detects the level of two female hormones associated with the start and end of her fertile period. This information is stored by the machine which then uses it to calculate the days when a woman is fertile and therefore should abstain from sexual intercourse. *Persona* does not involve the use of chemicals but it must be used every day, and the starter pack costs about £65 and £10 per month thereafter.[101] Moreover, it is not suitable for all women, such as those who are breastfeeding, using other hormones, or have either a very short or very long interval between periods. At present sixty-three women, who became pregnant after using *Persona*, are suing its manufacturer, the company Unipath. Each woman is claiming up to £150,000 in damages for an unsatisfactory product. According to press reports, in 1998 a review by the health watchdog Medical Devices Agency found that one in seventeen women using the *Persona* would become pregnant in a year.[102]

4) The *rhythm method*,[103] like *Persona*, also involves abstaining from sexual intercourse or using alternative contraception during a woman's fertile period. There are several techniques that may be used.

- The *calendar rhythm method* uses calendar calculations to determine the fertile time.
- The *temperature method* (also known as BBT, basal body temperature) relies on the detection of the small change in body temperature that takes place after an egg has been released.
- The *Billings method* involves studying cervical mucus which undergoes a change shortly before an egg is released. The Billings method is now available in conjunction with a computer software package known as the WinBOM Charting System.[104]

- The *sympto-thermal method* involves a woman monitoring, amongst other things, symptoms such as mood swings, breast sensitivity, body temperature, and changes in cervical mucus.

A variation of the rhythm method is the *Lady-Comp*.[105] This device uses the temperature method and compares it with a database of thousands of other women's cycles. A red light means 'no sexual intercourse' or 'use another contraceptive method'; a green light means that 'it is safe to have unprotected sexual intercourse'; and a yellow light means it is 'uncertain' and, therefore, 'unsafe to have unprotected sexual intercourse'. The manufacturers, Valley Electronics, claim that *Lady-Comp* has a failure rate of 0.7%.[106] The *Lady-Comp* data costs about £300.[107]

A less sophisticated version of this method involves CycleBeads. This is a 32-bead loop that has twelve white beads, which glow in the dark and represent days when the woman may be fertile, a red bead, for the start of the cycle, and brown beads denoting when pregnancy is very unlikely. This method, which is based on a sophisticated computer analysis of women's menstrual cycles, is best for women with a menstrual cycle lasting between 26 to 32 days. A study from the United States of almost 500 women in Bolivia, Peru and the Philippines found the beads had a five percent failure rate.[108]

5) *Breastfeeding*. Most non-breastfeeding mothers will start their periods within 4 to 6 weeks of delivery. Two-thirds of these women will have ovulated prior to their first period. 45 days is the average time to first ovulation following childbirth.[109]

By contrast women who breastfeed can delay the onset of ovulation and their first period following childbirth. During a breastfeed, suckling by the infant causes a disruption in the normal production of hormones in the mother with the result that ovulation may be suppressed.

However, ovulation can occur in the breastfeeding mother irrespective of whether or not she has had a period. The probability of ovulation happening increases the older the baby is. Thus during the first 3 months, 33% to 45% of breastfeeding mothers will ovulate. This increases to 64% to 71% during the next 9 months. By a year, 87% to 100% of breastfeeding mothers would have ovulated.[110]

This is why the American College of Obstetricians and Gynecologists recommend that women who use breastfeeding as their only means of contraception limit this to 6 months. After 6 months breastfeeding mothers are advised to use an additional method.[111]

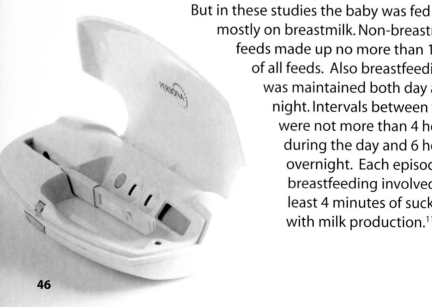

Studies have shown that breastfeeding gives more than 98% protection from pregnancy in the first 6 months. But in these studies the baby was fed mostly on breastmilk. Non-breastmilk feeds made up no more than 10% of all feeds. Also breastfeeding was maintained both day and night. Intervals between feeds were not more than 4 hours during the day and 6 hours overnight. Each episode of breastfeeding involved at least 4 minutes of suckling with milk production.[112]

Female Sterilisation

Failure Rates
Perfect use = 0.5%
Typical use = 0.5%

Description
Female sterilisation is the most common method of contraception used by married or cohabiting women worldwide.[113] The General Household Survey found that nine percent of women in Great Britain opt for this method of contraception.[114] It is meant to be a permanent method although in a small number of women it can be successfully reversed. However, this reversal is a major operation and requires a high level of expertise.

When sterilisation is reversed between 31% and 92% become pregnant.[115] But of these women who have a reversal and who become pregnant between 2% and 12.5% will have an ectopic pregnancy.[116]

This method cannot destroy an embryo and so in that sense it is pro-life. However there is a very small risk of an ectopic pregnancy following sterilisation. In this rare event an embryo would be lost. In addition the use of sterilisation raises other important ethical issues which are not discussed in this book.

Mode of Action
There are three main ways of performing a sterilisation. The first two are usually carried out under general anaesthetic.

1) Sterilisation may be achieved either by placing a ring/band or a clip over each fallopian tube or by electrically burning the tubes.[117] The latter method is now not recommended by the Royal College of Obstetricians and Gynaecologists because of the increased risk of ectopic pregnancies and because this method is difficult to reverse.[118]

2) A form of sterilisation, usually carried out upon request at the time of caesarean section, involves removing the mid-portion of each fallopian tube.[119]

3) The newest technique, which has undergone successful major trials in the United States,[120] is called *Essure®*. It involves placing tiny coils into each fallopian tube. It does not require a general anaesthetic and takes about 35 minutes. Over the 12 weeks following this procedure, scar tissue grows over the coils. This process should completely block the tubes. During the twelve week period, women are advised to use an alternative method of contraception. After three months, women have an X-ray taken. This is to ensure that the coils are in place and that the fallopian tubes are blocked. *Conceptus®*, the manufacturers of *Essure®*, claim that in clinical testing it was 99.8% effective after two years of follow up.[121]

Removing a portion of tube, or placing a structure over or within it produces a physical barrier between the egg and sperm and stops them meeting, so this method of contraception does not cause the loss of an embryo.

Side Effects
Minor side effects include a few days of mild abdominal cramps, and the effects of having had a general anaesthetic.[122] On rare occasions during the sterilisation operation, the bowels, bladder or major blood vessels are injured and require major surgical repair. If

injuries are not detected early enough, the woman may die from these major complications.[123] It has been estimated that 6% to 20% of women regret their loss of fertility.[124] The higher figure applies to women aged 30 years old or younger. If a woman does become pregnant after sterilisation it is more likely to be an ectopic pregnancy since the fallopian tube has been damaged during the sterilisation.[125]

Male Sterilisation (Vasectomy)[126]

Failure Rates
Perfect use = 0.10%
Typical use = 0.15%

Description
For twelve percent of women, their method of contraception is the fact that their husband or boyfriend has been sterilised.[127] Like female sterilisation this method of contraception is meant to be a permanent procedure. However, it too can be reversed, with the rate of successful births ranging from 38% to 82%. Pregnancy rates (as distinct from successful births) drop to less than 50% when reversal is performed more than 9 to 10 years after vasectomy.[128]

This method cannot destroy an embryo and so, in that sense, it is pro-life. However, the use of sterilisation raises other important ethical issues which are not discussed in this book.

Mode of Action[129]
Vasectomy is a minor surgical procedure that is usually carried out under local anaesthesia. There are two main techniques to find the vas deferens (the tube that carries sperm from the testes where sperm are made). In a conventional vasectomy one or two small cuts are made in the scrotal skin. Through the cuts the vas deferens is found. In 1974 a variation of this method called 'no scalpel vasectomy' (NSV) was developed in China. In this technique the vas deferens is held in place with a clamp before the scrotal skin is opened. A special instrument is used to make a tiny puncture in the

skin above the vas deferens. This tiny opening is then stretched in order to reach the vas deferens. In both techniques, either a small piece is taken out of the vas deferens or the tube may be burnt, clipped, divided or a combination of these. The procedure may take up to about 20 minutes.

Unlike a conventional vasectomy the wound produced during a NSV is so small that no sutures are required. NSV is also faster than a conventional vasectomy, less painful during the procedure and causes fewer complications.

Following a vasectomy a man is not considered to be sterile until his semen contains no sperm and this may take up to three months.

Side effects
Infection and bruising are the most common complications. Occasionally the cut end of the vas deferens may leak sperm and cause the formation of a painful swelling that generally subsides spontaneously.[130]

In the long-term men often develop antibodies to sperm. This is only important if the man wishes to have his vasectomy reversed because the antibodies destroy any sperm and therefore may prevent attempts to restore the man's fertility.[131]

In the past there was a suggestion that having a vasectomy increased the risk of developing prostate cancer, however more recent research has failed to support this theory.[132]

Buffergel™

This contraceptive gel is still undergoing clinical trials. It has been designed to protect women against pregnancy and from sexually transmitted infections such as HIV (which can lead to AIDS), herpes, chlamydia and the Human Papilloma Virus (HPV) which has been linked to cervical cancer. The gel works by boosting the acidity of the vagina, a condition that readily kills both sperm and infections. The gel, which is also available as a Buffergel cup™, is applied locally before sex.[133]

Other Male Contraception

Description
Scientists are developing hormonal contraception for men in the form of a three monthly injection,[134] an implant[135], and a patch/pill combination.[136] There is also an attempt to develop a non-hormonal drug as a daily pill.[137]

Mode of Action
The contraceptive pill, implant and patch, which contain hormones and are still under trial at present, work by stopping the production of sperm. Therefore, they would not cause the loss of an embryo.

Side Effects
Initial results in men show that these newer contraceptives work very well. However, one of their most common consequences is that men need to be given the male hormone testosterone as well as the contraceptive drug in order to maintain their sex drive.

Other experimental techniques
Since 1999 a Canadian company called Immucon[138] has been testing a contraceptive vaccine. The vaccine consists of a chemical, found in the body, that is involved in fertilisation. In theory, giving the vaccine should cause the body to see this chemical as foreign and, therefore, something that must be destroyed. This action would interfere with the chemical's normal function and therefore prevent fertilisation. Immucon claim that this effect is reversible and that it works for up to 12 months. This product would not cause the loss of an embryo if its only action were to prevent fertilisation.

A male contraceptive currently under trial in Asia is known as vas occlusion. It involves injecting a synthetic, plastic or silicon plug into the tube (the vas deferens) that carries sperm from the testis. The plug hardens and either forms a physical barrier against the sperm or affects the surface of the sperm so that they are incapable of fertilising an egg. This contraceptive method has various names such as Shug, MPU, MSR[139] and RISUG[140]. MPU and MSR plugs take six months to completely block 98% of sperm. Both the Shug plug and RISUG take two to three months to completely block 97 - 100% of sperm. These techniques are supposed to be reversible. Men who have had the MPU plug removed after five years have successfully conceived after the reversal procedure. Evidence for the reversibility of the other techniques has not been proven in humans yet.[141]

These products should not cause the loss of an embryo as their prime function is to prevent the passage of sperm.

Morning-after pill[142]

Failure Rate
0.4 – 2.7%[143]

Description
The original morning-after pill was called *PC4*, and consisted of a high dose of oestrogen combined with a high dose of a progestogen. This is no longer available. The only morning-after pill now available is the more recently introduced product, *Levonelle-2*. It can be obtained without a doctor's prescription and contains a high dose of a progestogen alone.

The morning-after pill is called "emergency contraception" because it is taken by a woman after she has had unprotected intercourse. However, its purpose is not just to stop conception. It also stops an established pregnancy from developing by causing the loss of an embryo.

Mode of Action
The morning-after pill acts in several ways. If conception has not taken place the pill prevents the egg and sperm meeting by:

1) delaying or stopping the release of an egg; and
2) slowing the movement of sperm.

If conception has taken place, the pill blocks normal processes so the early embryo is unable to implant in the womb and therefore is expelled or aborted.

If the embryo has already implanted in the womb, the morning-after pill will not cause it to be destroyed.

Side Effects

PC4 caused nausea and vomiting.[144] These side effects are much less common in women who use *Levonelle-2*. But *Levonelle-2* is associated with an increased risk of developing an ectopic pregnancy.[145]

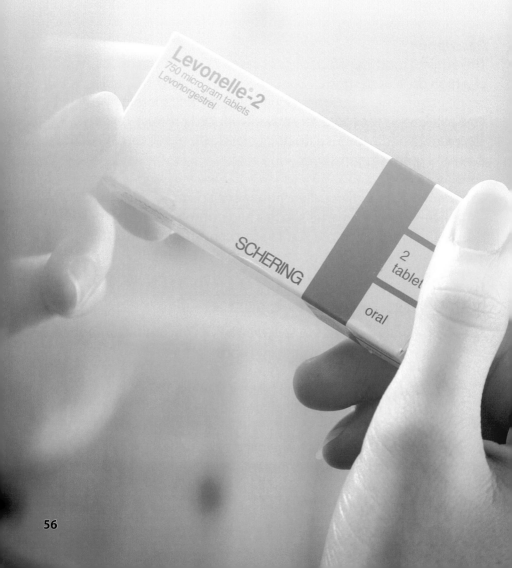

RU486
(also known as Mifepristone)

Description
This is not a contraceptive. It may be used to cause abortions up to the 24th week of pregnancy as an alternative to an operation. Beyond 24 weeks it can be used to induce labour after the fetus has died in the womb.[146] At present the British Pregnancy Advisory Service is campaigning for women in early pregnancy to carry out their own abortion by taking this abortion pill at home.[147] This is to "give women more control over their own abortion" and to "allow the most traumatic part of the procedure to take place in familiar surroundings".[148]

Mode of Action
Mifepristone stops the body from producing the hormone progesterone, which is needed to sustain the pregnancy. Another drug, Gemeprost, is then given that causes the neck of the womb to open, after which the pregnancy is aborted.[149]

Side effects
The side effects of mifepristone include pain and bleeding. One in a hundred women will require an operation to deal with the bleeding and one in a thousand a blood transfusion.[150]

Can the pill cause the loss of an embryo?

The combined oral contraceptive pill (commonly known as 'the pill') is one of the most popular methods of birth control. It became widely available in the 1960s. At that time it was said to work solely by preventing conception, mainly by stopping the release of eggs (ovulation). There was no suggestion that the pill could act to stop a newly conceived embryo from implanting in the womb. However, new information has caused some people to think again. This has led to a debate amongst pro-life doctors as to whether the pill is a secure pro-life method of contraception.[151]

One doctor has written, "Though I have long been aware of the controversy concerning whether the oral contraceptive pill (OCP) sometimes causes abortions, I have in the past year become increasingly familiar with the arguments alleging that the pill is sometimes abortifacient. Though I am concerned that some of the articles presenting such arguments refer loosely to "facts" that are somewhat inferential or cannot be readily verified, I am nevertheless hesitant to wholly disregard the possibility that the pill may at times cause the death of an early embryo."[152]

The pill works in three ways. Primarily, it works by stopping the release of eggs (ovulation). But it also has two secondary actions. It blocks the movement of sperm by thickening the cervical mucus and it thins the lining of the womb. Blocking the movement of the sperm causes no ethical problem for a pro-life user, but thinning the lining of the womb is a different matter. If ovulation occurs and if blocking the movement of the sperm fails, then thinning the lining of the womb may cause the death of an early embryo. Whether this actually happens is the subject of much controversy.

Can ovulation occur while on the pill?

The pill seems to be very effective at stopping the release of eggs. Nevertheless, there is evidence that ovulation can sometimes occur and changes over the years in the oestrogen dose of the pill may have influenced this. It is worth understanding that the pill has changed in its makeup since it became popular in the 1960s. Originally the pill contained between 100 and 175 micrograms of oestrogen (the principal component that stops ovulation). However, this level of oestrogen led to fears that the pill could cause blood clots, strokes or heart attacks in some women. The amount of oestrogen in the pill has been reduced typically to between 30 and 35 micrograms. For some women, it has even been reduced to as low as 20 micrograms. Manufacturers claim these lower-dose pills are still sufficient to stop ovulation. However, others say there is a risk, albeit a very small one, a lower-dose of oestrogen may increase the chances of unexpected ovulation.

Some studies suggest that ovulation can occur on the pill. One study looked at healthy women taking the low-dose pill (20 micrograms) over three cycles and used ultrasound and blood tests to see whether any ovulation took place. In such a closely-monitored short-term study it is likely that the pill was reliably taken by its subjects. Even in these circumstances it was found that ovulation still occurred in 2.7% of cycles.[153] However, other similar studies failed to show any ovulation occurring in women on the pill.[154]

Other strong evidence pointing to ovulation on the pill comes from the fact that women using the pill get pregnant.[155] Even the manufacturers admit a failure rate of 0.1% for women who take the pill 'perfectly' i.e. according to instructions and are in good health (the failure rate is the number of women becoming pregnant in the first year of use, in this case 1 pregnancy per 1,000 women in the first year). Some say this failure rate is exaggerated so that the manufacturers cover themselves legally.[156]

In reality, many will not take the pill 'perfectly'. It is more important to discover how effectively ovulation is prevented in real life (here studies use the term 'typical' use). Women may miss taking a pill (at perhaps an average number of 8 per year[157]) or have a medical condition such as gastro-enteritis which interferes with its effectiveness. The failure rate for this 'typical' use is 5%. Whatever else this may mean (and this will be discussed later) it certainly proves ovulation has occurred. However, in some well-defined forms of less than perfect use it seems that ovulation may be effectively prevented. One study of 99 women found no evidence of ovulation in women who missed the first pills of the cycle.[158]

In short, there is conflicting evidence as to how frequently ovulation on the pill may occur. For any individual woman during one cycle, ovulation seems unlikely, but there is no guarantee that over an extended time of pill usage this will not occur. And for pro-life couples, the next important question is to ask what happens if ovulation does occur.

Is the pill 100% effective in blocking sperm movement?
If ovulation does occur whilst on the pill, then a secondary action of the pill to block sperm movement may stop a conception. This works by thickening the cervical mucus. If this succeeds, it does not present an ethical problem to pro-life users. But it is not 100% successful. We know that the progestogen component of the combined pill acts to thicken the cervical mucus and so impede the movement of sperm.[159] However studies indicate that with the progestogen only pill (POP) in just 70-80% of cases sperm are blocked by the altered cervical mucus.[160] Similarly a study on the effect of progestogens and oestrogen on cervical mucus indicated that thickened cervical mucus does not result in all sperm being blocked.[161] This is further

demonstrated by the fact that some women get pregnant whilst on the pill.

So, if ovulation occurs and if blocking sperm mobility fails, a conception can take place. The key question now is, what happens to the newly conceived embryo? This is where the ethical problems start.

Can thinning the lining of the womb and other factors lead to the loss of an embryo?

The process of embryo implantation into the lining of the womb (the endometrium) is complex and now better understood as a result of research into in-vitro fertilisation (IVF)[162]. There is still much to learn but it has become clear that embryo implantation could be threatened in a number of ways.

The process is vulnerable at the molecular level when the embryo 'docks' with the endometrium. As many as 30 special hormones called 'implantation factors' may be involved as signals are sent out and received. It is possible that many other hormones including the oestrogens in the pill could interfere with this process.[163] However, at the moment techniques for observing implantation are not well enough advanced to support or refute such suggestions from laboratory studies.

Above the molecular scale, we know that the pill causes the endometrium to thin, although this is not the primary action of the pill. That this happens is not in dispute by anyone. The question is whether thinning the lining of the womb may cause the loss of an embryo. Some manufacturers seem to believe it does. In the words of one of them the effect of the pill is the "…rendering of the endometrium unreceptive to implantation".[164] Also, the *Handbook of Clinical Drug Data* says the pill works to "produce a thinning endometrium that hampers implantation".[165] This is also supported by the *Physicians' Desk Reference* in the United States.[166]

However not all scientists agree with these assertions. Evidence has been presented for[167] and against[168] the association between reduced endometrial thickness and reduced receptivity to implantation. Some infertility researchers (who are very interested in why some embryos implant and others don't) suggest that the thickness of the endometrium is a significant factor. One study of women receiving infertility treatment found that none conceived if their endometrium was less than 5mm thick.[169] Evidence shows that the endometrium of pill users may be as thin as 1.1mm, compared to between 3.1mm and 5mm for non-pill users.[170]

However, this study of the thickness of the endometrium in pill users did not look at pill users who were ovulating. This could make a crucial difference. It is argued that, if ovulation leads to a conception whilst on the pill, a natural burst of hormones will be released as normal. This natural burst of hormones may override the effects of the pill on the endometrium and cause it to thicken sufficiently to receive an embryo. Supporters of this position say there is no evidence to prove that the pill alters what naturally takes place. This suggestion is supported by the fact that successful pregnancies can occur in women who are on the pill. The assumption that the endometrium is always receptive for a woman who becomes pregnant on the pill is contradicted by a study that shows the endometrium of a woman who ovulates whilst on the pill remains thin and inactive even after ovulation[171] (but this study used a non-standard measure for deciding that ovulation had occurred).

Another argument supports the suggestion that the pill may cause the loss of an embryo. Of women who get pregnant, there is a certain ratio between the number of pregnancies outside the womb (ectopic pregnancies) and the number of pregnancies that develop normally in the womb (intrauterine pregnancies). If the pill has no affect on the implantation of an embryo, then the ratio should also be the same for women who get pregnant whilst on the pill. However, one study showed proportionately more ectopic pregnancies amongst women who had been on the pill prior to conceiving. This suggests that taking the pill was causing a loss of intrauterine pregnancies.[172] However, this study has been criticised because it was based on only 11 patients. Supporters of the pill say there is no evidence that the ratio is affected by the pill.

If the pill does cause the loss of an embryo by preventing it from implanting in the womb then how will the user know? How will the user be able to tell the difference between the loss of an embryo and the pill simply doing its job of blocking ovulation? From the manufacturer's point of view, the end result is the same – no pregnancy.

So what does it all mean?
Is the pill an ethical method of contraception for pro-life couples? There is evidence on both sides. Certainly, ovulation seems sometimes possible when on the pill. If the pill fails to block ovulation, then it may sometimes block the movement of sperm and therefore stop a conception, but sometimes it won't. If a conception does occur then there are two schools of thought about what happens next. Some say don't worry, a natural burst of hormones will kick in to override the effects of the pill on the lining of the womb and ensure the embryo has a normal chance of implanting. But others reject that. They say the pill thins the lining of the womb and keeps it thin even after a conception because natural hormones take longer to act. It could therefore cause the loss of an embryo.

It should be stressed that the pill almost invariably successfully stops ovulation. In the rare event that ovulation isn't stopped and a conception occurs, that is when the ethical problems start. At this time, it is impossible to say with certainty whether the pill causes the loss of an embryo. It can only be said that there is some evidence to suggest it is a possibility. If it does cause the loss of an embryo, it is not known how often this may occur.

Undoubtedly, there is a paucity of evidence to support the theory that the pill causes the loss of an embryo. Until the recent interest in IVF, the medical community has shown little interest in conducting studies on embryo implantation. In the years ahead there may be new studies which shed light on this question.

In 1999 some pro-life doctors in the U.S., convened by Focus on the Family, began to examine the question of whether the pill could cause the loss of an embryo. This was their conclusion:

> "The PRC [Physicians Resource Council] has carefully and conscientiously studied this issue and its members have come to different conclusions regarding the interpretation and implications of the relevant scientific data. After two years of extended deliberation, they have not been able to reach a consensus as to the likelihood, or even the possibility, that these medications might contribute to the loss of human life after fertilization. The majority of the physicians feel that the pill does not have an abortifacient effect. A minority of the doctors feel that when conception occurs on the pill, there is enough of a possibility for an abortifacient effect, however remote, to warrant informing women about it."[173]

Pro-life status summary

Condom ✓

Femidom® ✓

Diaphragm, cap, sponge ✓

Spermicide ✓

Progestogen-only pill ✗

Cerazette®

Combined oral contraceptive pill

Tricycling of the combined oral contraceptive pill (Tricycle regimen) ✓

Intrauterine contraceptive device - Copper containing coil ✗

Intrauterine contraceptive device - Mirena® intrauterine system ✗

Implanon®, Norplant

More frequent replacement of the hormone implant ✓

Depo-provera, Noristerat

More frequent injections (Depo-provera) ✓

Natural birth control ✓

Female sterilisation ✓

Male sterilisation (vasectomy) ✓

Buffergel™ (NEW!)

Other male contraception (NEW!)

Morning-after pill ✗

RU486 (also known as Mifepristone) ✗

References

1 Encyclical Letter from the Bishops with the Resolutions and Reports, Lambeth Conference, SPCK, 1930, pages 43-44. See also Noonan, J T, Contraception, A History of its Treatment by the Catholic Theologians and Canonists, Harvard University Press, 1966, page 409

2 Hatcher R A, Trussell J, Stewart F et al, Contraceptive Technology, Ardent Media, Inc, 2004, pages 792 - 845

3 House of Commons, Hansard, 19 July 2000, col. 221 wa

4 Hatcher R A, Trussell J, Stewart F et al, Contraceptive Technology, Ardent Media, Inc, 2004, page 345

5 Szarewski, A and Guillebaud, J, Contraception: A User's Guide, Oxford University Press, 2000, page 137

6 Hatcher R A, Trussell J, Stewart F et al, Contraceptive Technology, Ardent Media, Inc, 2004, page 373

7 Szarewski, A and Guillebaud, J, Op cit, page 154

8 Hatcher R A, Trussell J, Stewart F et al, Contraceptive Technology, Ardent Media, Inc, 2004, page 369

9 CNN.com, 'Today Sponge Goes On Sale Again', 5 March 2003, see http://www.cnn.com/2003/HEALTH/03/05/sponge.returns.ap/index.html as at 10 March 2003

10 Hatcher R A, Trussell J, Stewart F et al, Contraceptive Technology, Ardent Media, Inc, 2004, page 374 and Merck Manual of Diagnosis and Therapy, Section 13, Chapter 157, see http://www.merck.com/mrkshared/CVMHighLight?file=/mrkshared/mmanual/section13/chapter157/157a.jsp%3Fregion%3Dmerckcom&word=toxic&word=shock&word=syndrome&domain=www.merck.com#hl_anchor as at 9 September 2004

11 Information for Patients Using Orthoforms™ Contraceptive Pessaries, Janssen-Cilag Limited, June 2002.
    See also Hatcher R A, Trussell J, Stewart F et al, Contraceptive Technology, Ardent Media, Inc, 2004, page 358
    According to the Center for Disease Control

"...spermicides alone are not recommended for STD/HIV prevention. Frequent use of spermicides containing N-9 [Nonoxynol-9] has been associated with genital lesions, which may be associated with an increased risk of HIV transmission." Workowski, K A and Levine, W C, 'Sexually Transmitted Diseases Treatment Guidelines - 2002', Morbidity and Mortality Weekly Report, May 10, 2002 / 51(RR06);1-80 (see http://www.cdc.gov/mmwr/preview/mmwrhtml/rr5106a1.htm as at 25 February 2005). This risk applies to those whose behaviour exposes them to sexually transmitted diseases.

12 Hatcher R A, Trussell J, Stewart F et al, Contraceptive Technology, Ardent Media, Inc, 2004, pages 359 - 360

13 Hatcher R A, Trussell J, Stewart F et al, Contraceptive Technology, BMJ Books, 1998, page 216, These figures are taken from the 17th edition of Contraceptive Technology. In the latest edition (18th) failure rates for both the combined and progestogen-only pill have been combined. They are as follows. Perfect use = 0.3%; Typical use = 8%. See Hatcher R A, Trussell J, Stewart F et al, Contraceptive Technology, Ardent Media, Inc, 2004, pages 463-464. It is important to remember that the progestogen-only pill is less effective than the combined pill at preventing pregnancy. Therefore the combined pill would have a much lower 'typical use' failure rate than 8% and the progestogen-only pill would not have as low a 'perfect use' failure rate as 0.3%.

14 Guillebaud, J, Contraception: Your Questions Answered, Churchill Livingstone, 2004, page 283

15 Hatcher R A, Trussell J, Stewart F et al, Contraceptive Technology, Ardent Media, Inc, 2004, page 462

16 Chang M C and Hunt D M, 'Effects of Various Progestins and Estrogen on The Gamete Transport and Fertilization in The Rabbit', Fertility and Sterility, 21(9), 1970, pages 683-686

17 Martinez-manautou J, Continous Low Dose

Progestogen for Contraception, *International Planned Parenthood Federation*, 2(5), 1968 pages 2-3.

[18] Abdalla H I, Brooks A A, Johnson M R et al, 'Endometrial Thickness: A Predictor of Implantation in Ovum Recipients?' *Human Reproduction*, 9(2), 1994, pages 363-365 Bergh C, Hillensjö, T, Nilsson L, 'Sonographic Evaluation of the Endometrium in In Vitro Fertilisation IVF Cycles: A Way to Predict Pregnancy?' *Acta Obstetricia et Gynecologica Scandinavica*, 71, 1992, pages 624-628

[19] Sweetman, S C (ed), *Martindale: The Complete Drug Reference*, Pharmaceutical Press, 2005, page 1527

[20] Waiting until after the second period is likely to show that the process of ovulation and the normal thickening of the endometrium has returned.

[21] *British National Formulary*: 48 Edition, British Medical Association and Royal Pharmaceutical Society of Great Britain, 2004, Section 7.3.2.1, see http://www.bnf.org/bnf/bnf/current/noframes/4573.htm as at 14 September 2004 and Szarewski, A and Guillebaud, J, *Op cit*, page 90

[22] *British National Formulary*: 48 Edition, *Op cit*, Section 7.3.2.1

[23] Information on Cerazette® is from data information sheet from Organon Laboratories Limited

[24] Data information sheet from Organon Laboratories Limited

[25] Free communication at the 8th European Society of Contraception Congress, 'Maintenance of Consistent Ovulation Inhibition with the 75 mcg Desogestrel-Only Contraceptive Pill Cerazette® After Scheduled 12-Hour Delay in Tablet Intake', see http://www.contraception-esc.com/congress/abstract/fc407.htm as at 15 September 2004

[26] Patient information sheet, Organon Laboratories Limited, June 2004

[27] Guillebaud, J, 'When Do Contraceptives Work?' *Triple Helix*, Summer 2003, pages 12-13

[28] We also note that John Guillebaud uses similar arguments to us in respect of the Mirena® Interuterine System. Consistently applied, this argument also applies to Cerazette®.

[29] Waiting until after the second period is likely to show that the process of ovulation and the

normal thickening of the endometrium has returned.

[30] Patient information sheet, Organon Laboratories Limited, June 2004

[31] Hatcher R A, Trussell J, Stewart F et al, *Contraceptive Technology*, BMJ Books, 1998, page 216. The figures are taken from the 17th edition of *Contraceptive Technology*. In the latest edition (18th) failure rates for both the combined and progestogen-only pill have been combined. They are as follows. Perfect use = 0.3%; Typical use = 8%. See Hatcher R A, Trussell J, Stewart F et al, *Contraceptive Technology*, Ardent Media, Inc, 2004, page 792. It is important to remember that the progestogen-only pill is less effective than the combined pill at preventing pregnancy. Therefore the combined pill would have a much lower 'typical use' failure rate than 8% and the progestogen-only pill would not have as low a 'perfect use' failure rate as 0.3%.

[32] Guillebaud, J, *Contraception: Your Questions Answered*, *Op cit*, page 255

[33] Waiting until after the second period is likely to show that the process of ovulation and the normal thickening of the endometrium has returned.

[34] *British National Formulary*: 48 Edition, *Op cit*, Section 7.3.1

[35] In healthy non-pregnant women not taking the pill there are about 5 cases of thrombosis per 100,000 women per year. In woman taking COCPs which contain the progestogen levonorgestrel there are about 15 cases of thrombosis per 100,000 women per year. Patient Information Leaflet for Microgynon® 30, Schering Health Care Limited, June 2003

[36] Patient Information Leaflet for Microgynon® 30, Schering Health Care Limited, June 2003

[37] Patient Information Leaflet for Microgynon® 30, Schering Health Care Limited, June 2003

[38] Data information sheet from Schering Limited

[39] Scottish Medicines Consortium, Press Release, *The Scottish Consortium Issues Advice on Drospirenone Ethinylestradiol (Yasmin®) for Oral Contraception*, 7 March 2003

[40] van Grootheest K, and Vrieling T, 'Thromboembolism Associated with the New Contraceptive Yasmin', *British Medical Journal*, 326, 2003, page 257

[41] Medicines and Healthcare Products Regulatory Agency, *Current Problems in*

Pharmacovigilance, Vol. 30, October 2004

[42] Faculty of Family Planning and Reproductive Health Care Clinical Effectiveness Unit, Press Release, *New Product Review (September 2003): Norelgestromin/Ethinyloestradiol Transdermal Contraceptive System (Evra)*, 2003

[43] Data information sheet from Janssen-Cilag Limited

[44] See http://news.bbc.co.uk/1/hi/health/3672080.stm as at 22 September 2004

[45] *Daily Mail*, 8 December 2003 and BBC Online, 8 December 2003, see http://news.bbc.co.uk/1/hi/health/3300497.stm as at 15 September 2004

[46] *Daily Mail*, 13 July 2004

[47] Guillebaud, J, *Contraception: Your Questions Answered*, *Op cit*, pages 120-123

[48] Guillebaud, J, 'When Do Contraceptives Work?', *Op cit*, pages 12-13

[49] Guillebaud, J, *Contraception: Your Questions Answered*, *Op cit*, page 122 and pages 535-536

[50] Stanford J B, and Mikolajczyk R T, 'Mechanisms of Action of Intrauterine Devices: Update and Estimation of Postfertilization Effects', *American Journal of Obstetrics and Gynecology*, 187 (6), 2002, pages 1699-1708

[51] Guillebaud, J, *Contraception: Your Questions Answered*, *Op cit*, page 370

[52] Stanford J B, and Mikolajczyk R T, *Op cit*, pages 1699-1708

[53] *Loc cit*

[54] Guillebaud, J, *Contraception: Your Questions Answered*, *Op cit*, page 376

[55] Hatcher R A, Trussell J, Stewart F et al, *Contraceptive Technology*, Ardent Media, Inc, 2004, page 500

[56] *Loc cit*

[57] Guillebaud, J, *Contraception: Your Questions Answered*, *Op cit*, page 378

[58] *Ibid*, page 380

[59] *Ibid*, pages 402 - 403

[60] Hatcher R A, Trussell J, Stewart F et al, *Contraceptive Technology*, Ardent Media, Inc, 2004, page 237

[61] Data information sheet, Schering Health Care Limited

[62] Stanford J B, and Mikolajczyk R T, *Op cit*, pages 1699-1708

[63] Data information sheet, Schering Health Care Limited

[64] Barbosa I, Bakos O, Olsson S-E et al, 'Ovarian Function During Use of A Levonorgestrel-

releasing IUD', *Contraception*, 42(1), 1990, page 56

[65] Stanford J B, and Mikolajczyk R T, *Op cit*, pages 1699-1708

[66] Guillebaud, J, 'When Do Contraceptives Work?', *Op cit*, pages 12-13

[67] *Loc cit*

[68] *Loc cit*

[69] Guillebaud, J, *Contraception: Your Questions Answered*, *Op cit*, page 437

[70] Waiting until after the first period is likely to show that the process of ovulation and the normal thickening of the endometrium has returned.

[71] Guillebaud, J, *Contraception: Your Questions Answered*, *Op cit*, page 376; Patient Information Booklet, Schering Health Care Limited, July 2004 (This lists the problems of inserting the coil as affecting less than 1 in 1000 women).

[72] Hatcher R A, Trussell J, Stewart F et al, *Contraceptive Technology*, Ardent Media, Inc, 2004, page 500

[73] Guillebaud, J, *Contraception: Your Questions Answered*, *Op cit*, page 378

[74] Data information sheet, Schering Health Care Limited, The manufacturer states that the rate of ectopic pregnancy among users of copper containing coils is 0.12%.

[75] Szarewski, A and Guillebaud, J, *Op cit*, page 132

[76] Data information sheet, Schering Health Care Limited

[77] Croxatto H B and Makarainen L, 'The Pharmacodynamics and Efficacy of Implanon®. An Overview of The Data', *Contraception*, 58(6 Suppl), 1998, pages 91S-97S and Bennink H J T C, 'The Pharmacokinetics and Pharmacodynamics of Implanon®, a Single-Rod Etonorgestrel Contraceptive Implant', *European Jouranl of Contraception and Reproductive Health* Care, 5 (Suppl 2), 2000, pages 12-20

[78] Data information sheet, Organon Laboratories Limited

[79] Croxatto H B and Makarainen L, *Op cit*, pages 91S-97S

[80] *Loc cit*

[81] Bennink H J T C, 'The Pharmacokinetics and Pharmacodynamics of Implanon®, a Single-Rod Etonorgestrel Contraceptive Implant', *Op cit*, pages 12-20

82 Guillebaud, J, *Contraception: Your Questions Answered*, Op cit, page 350
83 Waiting until after the second period is likely to show that the process of ovulation and the normal thickening of the endometrium has returned.
84 Information for the Patient, Organon Laboratories Limited, July 2003
85 Data information sheet, Organon Laboratories Limited
86 Bennink H J T C, 'The Pharmacokinetics and Pharmacodynamics of Implanon®, a Single-Rod Etonorgestrel Contraceptive Implant', *Op cit*, pages 12-20
87 Data information sheet, Organon Laboratories Limited. The Data information sheet states "…the user should be informed that she can request the removal of Implanon® at any time."
88 Guillebaud, J, *Contraception: Your Questions Answered*, Op cit, page 321
89 *Ibid*, pages 320 – 321
90 *Ibid*, page 339. The median average is quoted. The mean average is 9 months.
91 Waiting until after the first period is likely to show that the process of ovulation and the normal thickening of the endometrium has returned.
92 Patient Information Leaflet, Pharmacia, July 2001
93 Guillebaud, J, *Contraception: Your Questions Answered*, Op cit, page 339
94 *Ibid*, pages 328 – 329
95 Morrison, C S, Bright, P, Wong, E L et al, Hormonal Contraceptive Use, Cervical Ectopy, and the Acquisition of Cervical infections, *Sexually Transmitted Diseases*, 31 (9), September 2004, pages 561 – 567 and Duerr, A, Warren, D, Smith, D et al, Contraceptives and HIV Transmission, *Nature Medicine*, 3 (2), February 1997, page 124
96 Guillebaud, J, *Contraception: Your Questions Answered*, Op cit, pages 320 – 321: Guillebaud states that follicular activity begins. While this does not necessarily lead to ovulation, he goes on to make a recommendation on the basis that it may.
97 Guillebaud, J, 'When Do Contraceptives Work?', *Op cit*, pages 12 - 13
98 Based on the claims of Unipath who make Persona, see http://www.persona.info/WhatisPersona3F.cfm as at 10 August 2004
99 Hatcher R A, Trussell J, Stewart F et al, *Contraceptive Technology*, Ardent Media, Inc, 2004, page 313
100 Guillebaud, J, *Contraception: Your Questions Answered*, Op cit, pages 44 - 45
101 See http://www.persona.info/Wherecanyoubuypersona3F.cfm as at 10 August 2004
102 *The Daily Telegraph*, 7 June 2002, *Daily Mail*, 7 June 2002, *The Times*, 7 June 2002.
103 Hatcher R A, Trussell J, Stewart F et al, *Contraceptive Technology*, Ardent Media, Inc, 2004, pages 317 - 319 and 'Natural Birth Control', see http://epigee.org/guide/natural.html as at 20 September 2004
104 *Scottish Catholic Observer*, 10 October 2003 and manufacturer's information sheet, see http://www.simlsystems.com/index.htm as at 20 September 2004
105 *The Independent*, 26 July 2004 and see http://www.babycomp-ladycomp.com/en/produkte/natuerlich/index.php as at 10 August 2004
106 'Safety of Contraception', see http://www.bc-lc.com/cgi-bin/print.pl?/en/planung/pearl/index.php as at 10 August 2004
107 Price List, see http://www.bc-lc.com/cgi-bin/print.pl?/en/beratung/bestellen/formular.php as at 10 August 2004
108 *The Scotsman*, 12 June 2002 and Arévalo M, Jennings V, Sinai I, 'Efficacy of a New Method of Family Planning: The Standard Days Method', *Contraception*, 65(5), 2002, pages 333 - 338
109 Hatcher R A, Trussell J, Stewart F et al, *Contraceptive Technology*, Ardent Media, Inc, 2004, page 576
110 *Ibid*, page 578
111 'Contraception While Breastfeeding', American College of Obstetricians and Gynecologists, see http://www.medem.com/MedLB/article_detaillb_for_printer.cfm?article_ID=ZZZ9XXA7AEC&sub_cat=4 as at 11 August 2004
112 'Contraception During Breastfeeding', *The Contraception Report*, 13(4), 2003, page 7 – 13 and 'Contraception While Breastfeeding', American College of Obstetricians and Gynecologists, see http://www.medem.com/MedLB/article_detaillb_for_printer.cfm?article_ID=ZZZ9XXA7AEC&sub_cat=4 as at 11 August 2004
113 Wise J, 'China is Top of Contraception League',

British Medical Journal, 313, 1996, page 135 and Hatcher R A, Trussell J, Stewart F et al, *Contraceptive Technology*, Ardent Media, Inc, 2004, page 531

[114] *Living in Britain: Results from the 2002 General Household Survey*, 31, ONS, The Stationery Office, 2004, table 10.1, page 181

[115] 'Male and Female Sterilisation: Evidence-Based Clinical Guideline Number 4', Royal College of Obstetricians and Gynaecologists, RCOG Press, 2004, page 38

[116] Hatcher R A, Trussell J, Stewart F et al, *Contraceptive Technology*, Ardent Media, Inc, 2004, page 563

[117] Szarewski, A and Guillebaud, J, *Op cit*, pages 202 – 204

[118] 'Male and Female Sterilisation: Evidence-Based Clinical Guideline Number 4', Royal College of Obstetricians and Gynaecologists, *Op cit*, page 28

[119] Hatcher R A, Trussell J, Stewart F et al, *Contraceptive Technology*, Ardent Media, Inc, 2004, page 549

[120] BBC News Online, 24 July 2002, see http://news.bbc.co.uk/1/hi/health/2146668.stm as at 17 August 2004 and MedicineNet.com, 4 November 2002 see http://www.medicinenet.com/script/main/art.asp?articlekey=21688 as at 27 September 2004

[121] 'Frequently Asked Questions' from the *Essure*® website, see http://www.essure.com/consumer/c_faq.aspx#faq12 as at 17 August 2004

[122] Szarewski, A and Guillebaud, J, *Op cit*, page 205

[123] 'Male and Female Sterilisation: Evidence-Based Clinical Guideline Number 4', Royal College of Obstetricians and Gynaecologists, *Op cit*, pages 29 - 30

[124] Hillis S D, Marchbanks P A, Ratliff Tylor L et al, 'PostSterilization Regret: Findings From the United States Collaborative Review of Sterilization', *Obstetrics and Gynecology*, 93 (6), 1999, pages 889 – 895

[125] 'Male and Female Sterilisation: Evidence-Based Clinical Guideline Number 4', Royal College of Obstetricians and Gynaecologists, *Op cit*, page 34

[126] This does not include the reversible methods mentioned in the section 'Other Male Contraception'

[127] *Living in Britain: Results from the 2002 General Household Survey*, *Op cit*, table 10.1, page 181

[128] Hatcher R A, Trussell J, Stewart F et al, *Contraceptive Technology*, Ardent Media, Inc, 2004, page 563

[129] 'Contraceptive Sterilization: Global Issues and Trends', EngenderHealth, 2002, New York, pages 164 – 165

[130] Hatcher R A, Trussell J, Stewart F et al, *Contraceptive Technology*, Ardent Media, Inc, 2004, page 562

[131] *Ibid*, page 539

[132] *Loc cit*

[133] *Daily Mail*, 7 January 2003

[134] *Daily Mail*, 6 October 2003, *The* Times, 7 October 2003, *The Daily Telegraph*, 7 October 2003, *The Herald*, 6 October 2003

[135] *The Herald*, 12 July 2001, *The Daily Telegraph*, 11 July 2001, *Daily Mail*, 20 May 2002, *Sunday Herald*, 19 May 2002, *The Herald*, 26 November 2003, *Daily Mail*, 26 February 2004, *The Scotsman*, 26 February 2004

[136] *Doctor's Guide*, 16 June 1999, see http://www.docguide.com/dg.nsf/PrintPrint/8067DDE274CB3BFB85256792004FDB33 as at 9 August 2004

[137] van der Spoel A C, Jeyakumar M, Butters T D et al, 'Reversible Infertility in Male Mice after Oral Administration of Alkylated Imino Sugars: A Nonhormonal Approach to Male Contraception', *Proceedings of the National Academy of Sciences*, 99 (26), 2002, pages 17173 - 17178

[138] *New York Post*, 13 July 1999, *PR Newswire*, 12 July 1999

[139] MPU = medical-grade polyurethane, MSR = medical-grade silicone rubber, these terminologies are referring to plugs that are used to block the vas deferens.

[140] RISUG = reversible inhibition of sperm under guidance

[141] Lohiya N K, Manivannan B, Mishra P K et al, 'Vas Deferens, A Site of Male Contraception: An Overview', *Asian Journal of Andrology*, 3, 2001, pages 87 – 95
Methods - vas devices – MPU and MS, see http://www.malecontraceptive.org/methods/mpu_frame.html as at 10 August 2004
Methods – vas devices – Shug, see http://www.malecontraceptive.org/methods/shug_frame.html as at 10 August 2004

Methods – vas devices – RISUG, see http://www.malecontraceptives.org/methods/risug_frame.html as at 10 August 2004

[142] See also The Christian Institute booklet on the morning after pill

[143] Guillebaud, J, *Contraception: Your Questions Answered*, *Op cit*, page 459

[144] Grimes D, von Hertzen H, Piaggio G et al, 'Randomised Controlled Trial of Levonorgestrel Versus The Yuzpe Regimen of Combined Oral Contraceptives for Emergency Contraception', *The Lancet*, 352 (9126), 1998, page 428 – 433

[145] 'Levonelle/Levonelle-2 Emergency Contraception: New Advice', *CMO's update 35*, January 2003, page 9

[146] *British National Formulary*: *48 Edition*, *Op cit*, Section 7.1.2

[147] *Daily Mail*, 9 August 2004

[148] *Daily Mail*, 9 August 2004

[149] *British National Formulary*: *48 Edition*, *Op cit*, Section 7.3.2.1

[150] Hatcher R A, Trussell J, Stewart F et al, *Contraceptive Technology*, Ardent Media, Inc, 2004, page 687

[151] This appendix can only attempt to summarise the key issues in the debate. For more information see the collection of papers in Bevington, L K and DiSilvestro, R (eds), *The Pill: Addressing the Scientific and Ethical Questions of the Abortifacient Issue*, The Centre for Bioethics and Human Dignity, undated. The main paper arguing that there is no abortifacient effect with the combined oral contraceptive pill is by Crockett S A, Harrison D, DeCook J L et al, *Hormone Contraceptives: Controversies and Clarifications*. (This paper is also available at www.aaplog.org/decook.htm as at 10 January 2005). The position taken by The Christian Institute is that life is sacred from conception. We believe that amongst those who hold this position there is a genuine debate to be had about whether the combined oral contraceptive has an abortifacient effect. But we do not believe that the same level of uncertainty applies with the progestogen only pill (POP). We therefore disagree with the clear implication of the paper by Susan Crockett and her colleagues that the POP is a legitimate pro-life option. We note what John Gillibaud states "…the progestogen only pill (POP) sometimes acts post-fertilisation. It permits ovulation in many cycles. Reduced sperm-penetrability of cervico-uterine mucus is unlikely to explain all the failures to conceive in the presence of ovulation. As with IUCDs, the occurrence of ectopic pregnancies provides further evidence, though not proof, of this." Guillebaud, J, 'When Do Contraceptives Work?', *Op cit*, pages 12-13

[152] Bevington L K and DiSilvestro R (eds), *Op cit*, page 16

[153] Coney, P and DelConte, A 'The Effects on Ovarian Activity of a Monophasic Oral Contraceptive with 100 microg Levonorgestrel and 20 microg Ethinyl Estradiol', *American Journal of Obstetrics and Gynecology*, 181 (5 Pt 2), November 1999, pages 53-58

[154] See, for example, Rossmanith, W G, Steffens, D and Schramm, G, 'A Comparative Randomized Trial on the Impact of Two Low-Dose Oral Contraceptives on Ovarian Activity, Cervical Permeability, and Endometrial Receptivity', *Contraception*, 56 (1), July 1997, pages 23-30; Wenzl, R, Bennink, H C, van Beek, A et al, 'Ovulation Inhibition with a Combined Oral Contraceptive Containing 1mg Micronized 17 -estradiol', *Fertility and Sterility*, 60 (4), October 1993, pages 616-619; and van Heusden, A M and Fauser, B C J M, 'Activity of the Pituitary-Ovarian Axis in the Pill-Free Interval During Use of Low-Dose Combined Oral Contraceptives', *Contraception*, 59 (PT 4), 1999, pages 237-243

[155] In a review of 25 studies, seven studies reported a total of 8 ovulations from 2910 cycles, and the remaining eighteen studies reported no ovulations from 3799 cycles. These 25 studies used a variety of low-dose pills (20 micrograms to 35 micrograms). See Crockett S A, Harrison D, DeCook J L et al, *Hormone Contraceptives: Controversies and Clarifications*, reproduced in Bevington, L K and DiSilvestro, R (eds), *Op cit*, page 79

[156] Bevington, L K and DiSilvestro, R (eds), *Op cit*, page 24

[157] Guillebaud, J, *Contraception: Your Questions Answered*, *Op cit*, page 120. The modal average is quoted.

[158] Elomaa, K, Rolland, R, Brosens, I et al, 'Omitting the First Oral Contraceptive Pills of the Cycle Does Not Automatically Lead to Ovulation',

American Journal of Obstetrics and Gynecology, 179 (1), July 1998, pages 41-46

[159] Hatcher R A, Trussell J, Stewart F et al, Contraceptive Technology, Ardent Media, Inc, 2004, page 392

[160] Crockett S A, Harrison D, DeCook J L et al, Hormone Contraceptives: Controversies and Clarifications, reproduced in Bevington, L K and DiSilvestro, R (eds), Op cit, page 80, see also Martinez-Manautou, J, Giner-Velasquez, J, Cortes-Gallegos, V et al, 'Daily Progestogen for Contraception: A clinical Study', British Medical Journal, 2, June 1967, pages 730-732

[161] Chang M C and Hunt D M, Op cit, pages 683-686

[162] Norwitz, E R, Schust, D J, and Fisher, S J, 'Mechanisms of Disease: Implantation and the Survival of the Early Pregnancy', New England Journal of Medicine, 345(19), 8 November 2001, pages 1400-1408.

[163] Wilks, J, 'The Impact of the Pill on Implantation Factors – New Research Findings', Ethics and Medicine, 16 (1), 2000, pages 15 - 22

[164] Data information sheet for Microgynon® 30, Schering Health Care Limited; Data information sheet for Brevinor, Pharmacia Limited; Data information sheet for Eugynon 30, Schering Health Limited; Data information sheet for Femodene, Schering Health Limited; Data information sheet for Logynon ED, Schering Health Limited; and Data information sheet for Norimin, Pharmacia Limited

[165] Anderson P O, Knoben, J E and Troutman, W G (eds), Handbook of Clinical Drug Data, McGraw-Hill, 2002, page 661

[166] Bevington, L K and DiSilvestro, R (eds), Op cit, page 23

[167] Abdalla, H I, Brooks, A A, Johnson, M R et al, Op cit, pages 363-365; and McCarthy, S, Tauber, C and Gore, J, 'Female Pelvic Anatomy: MR Assessment of Variations During the Menstrual Cycle and With Use of Oral Contraceptives', Radiology, 160, 1986, pages 119-123

[168] Crockett S A, Harrison D, DeCook J L et al, Hormone Contraceptives: Controversies and Clarifications, reproduced in Bevington, L K and DiSilvestro, R (eds), Op cit, pages 71-95.

[169] Abdalla, H I, Brooks, A A, Johnson, M R et al, Op cit, pages 363-365

[170] McCarthy, S, Tauber, C and Gore, J, Op cit, pages 119-123

[171] Chowdhury, V, Joshi, U M, Gopalkrishna, K et al, "Escape' Ovulation in Women Due to the Missing of Low Dose Combination Oral Contraceptive Pills', Contraception, 22 (3), July 1980, pages 241-247

[172] Coste, J, Job-Spira, N, Fernandez, H et al, 'Risk Factors for Ectopic Pregnancy: A Case-Control Study in France, with Special Focus on Infectious Factors', American Journal of Epidemiology, 133 (9), May 1991, pages 839-849

[173] Birth Control Pills, Focus on Your Family's Health, June 2004, see http://health.family.org/women_men/articles/a0002300.html as at 4 January 2005